Tony Hall:

A lifetime in cartoons

ISBN: 1 898231 23 0

Published by
Union Books
London WC1N 3XX
November 2009

Printed by:
Set Line Data Ltd
London SE16 3LL

1

4

5

7

9

I HEAR THEY CALL IT, THE THIRD WAY.

"TRY TO LOOK AT IT AS A SORT OF EARLY CONTRIBUTION TO THE 'TRICKLE DOWN FEEL GOOD FACTOR.'"

11

21

23

28

29

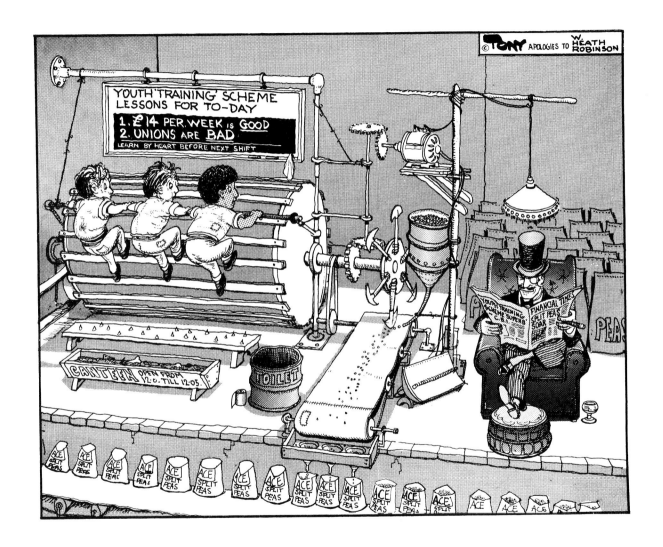

33

37

'And now for the GOOD news, we're building you some WONDERFUL new jails'

43

44

46

47

58

HARRY POTTER? NO, HE'S OUR LATEST
SCIENCE TEACHER.

AND NOW— A FEW WORDS FROM OUR SPONSOR...

"YOU'LL NEED A FAR BIGGER HOLE THAN THAT THIS TIME"

70

71

74

75

...WELL, NOBODY'S GOING TO SHOOT ME, WITH PRESCOTT AS DEPUTY...

84

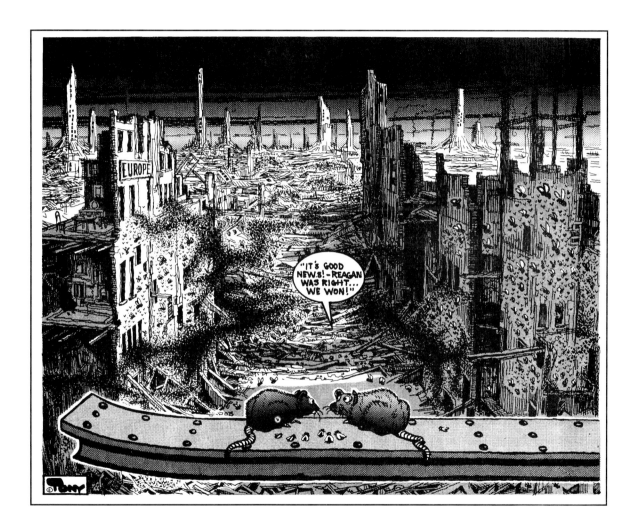

94

"IT'S OUR LATEST SCHEME, – WE'RE CALLING IT 'PUNISHMENT IN THE COMMUNITY'."

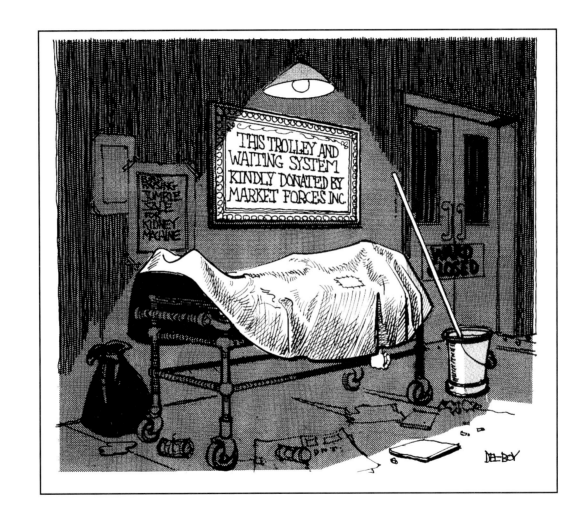

'Shhh, don't wake him up.'

110

111

'Far too much needless expenditure! WE'RE MOVING YOU INTO A SANDAL.'

114

"It's called freedom of choice Son -- CASH or ACCOUNT ?"

...I THINK IT'S MEANT TO REPRESENT AMERICAN SHELLFIRE...

WHAT AN AWFUL SHAME ... IT WAS SUCH A
WONDERFUL LIKENESS.

'Somehow I don't feel we're onto a winner here'